1 Constructing a block graph

Cycle fun

Constructing a block graph

Set	How many?
cones	
sticks	
balls	

Colour boxes to make a graph.

Obstacles graph

cones   sticks   balls

Birds

Classifying / recording / processing data

4

Look at the picture. Sort into 3 sets.

Set	How many?

Draw the graph.

Discuss your graph with a friend.

Big Eyes

Extension — Recording/displaying data

Look at the picture of Big Eyes.

Shapes	How many?
triangles	
rectangles	
pentagons	
hexagons	

Draw a graph.

Shapes graph

- triangles
- rectangles
- pentagons
- hexagons

Write about your graph.

Relationships

7

The picnic

Kay

Sam

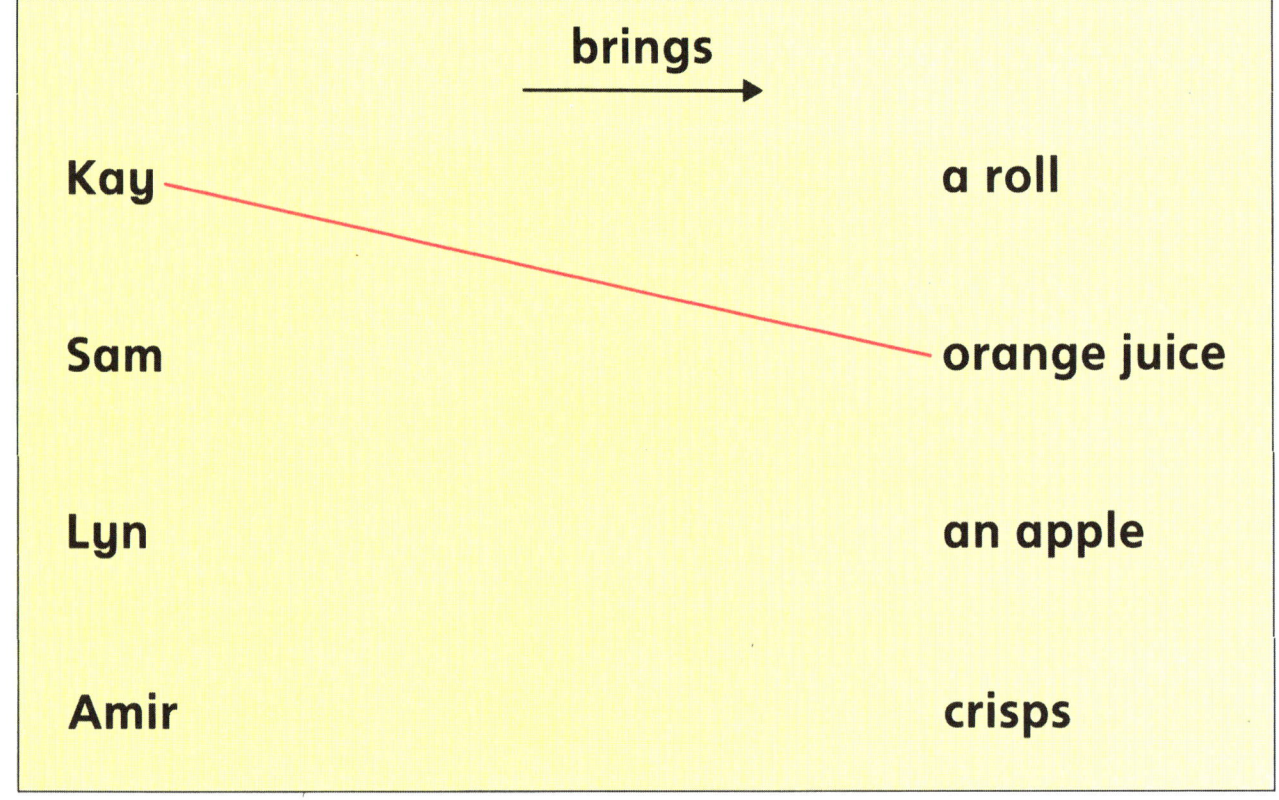

	brings →
Kay	a roll
Sam	orange juice
Lyn	an apple
Amir	crisps

Relationships

8

Lyn   Amir

Colour the shirts.

is coloured →

Kay's shirt — red

Sam's shirt — yellow

Lyn's shirt — blue

Amir's shirt — green

Our group

Find out about 8 children. Colour the chart.

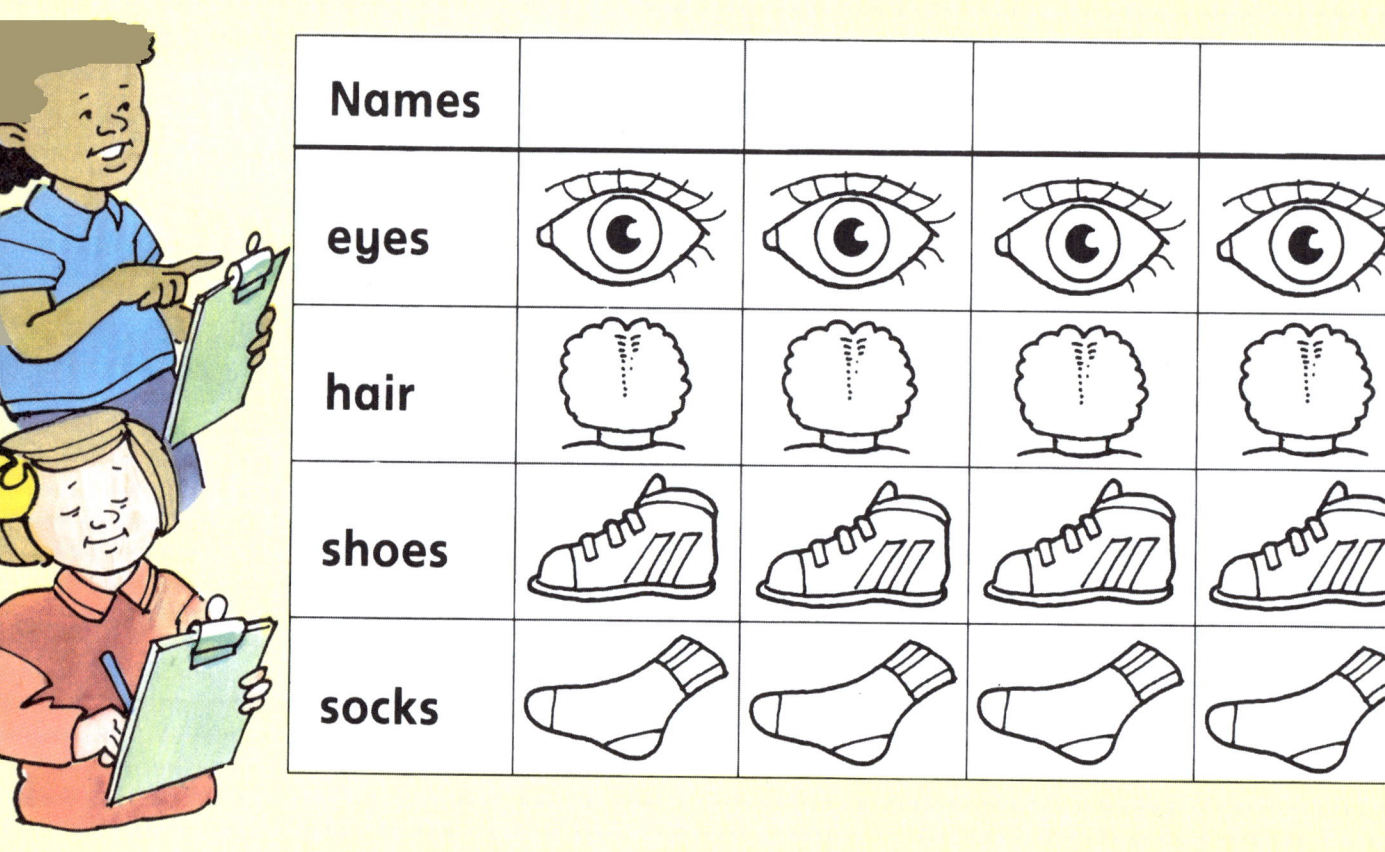

How many have blue eyes? ___

How many have black shoes? ___

How many have red socks? ___

How many have brown hair? ___

How many have brown eyes? ___

Investigation — Collecting and interpreting data

10

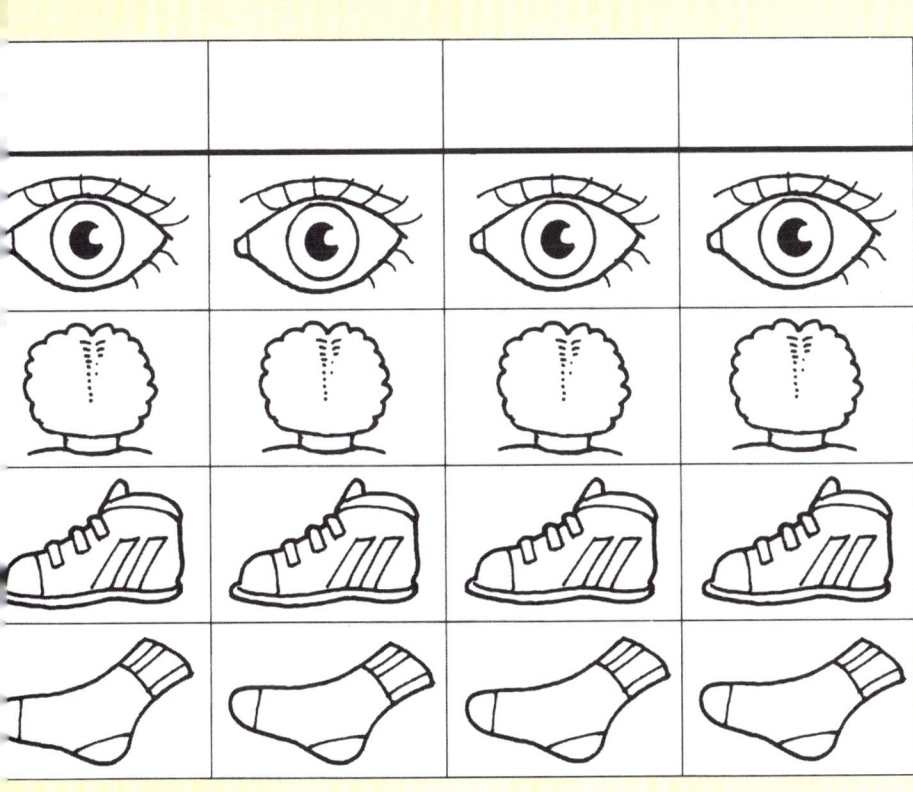

Who has brown hair and brown eyes?

Who has black shoes and white socks?

Investigation / Extension

Find out about the colour of schoolbags in your class.

Cubes

Alan and Tracy picked cubes out of a bag.

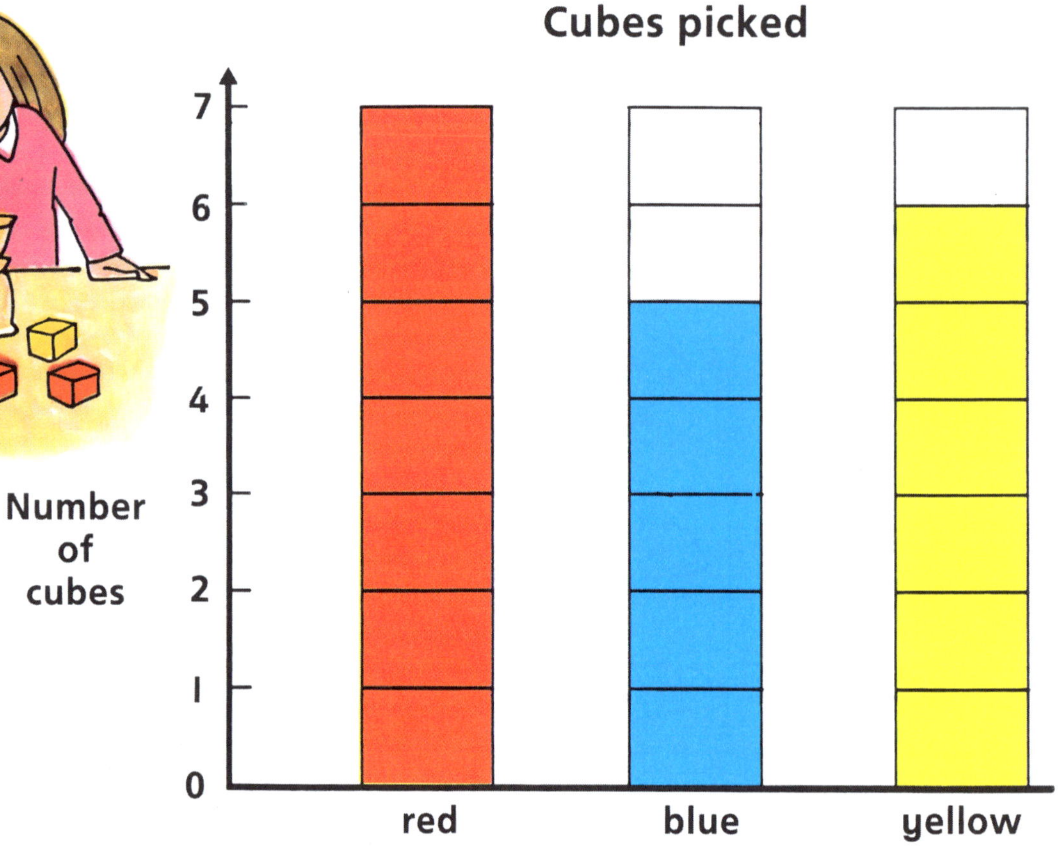

Cubes picked

Number of cubes: red 7, blue 5, yellow 6

How many more red than blue cubes? ____

How many cubes were picked altogether? ____

Extension / Problem solving

Alan picked these cubes. What did Tracy pick?

____ red cubes

____ blue cubes

____ yellow cubes

Constructing a frequency table

You need the bag of cubes.

Pick a cube. Tick its colour.
Do this until the bag is empty.

Colour	Ticks (✓)	Number of cubes
red		
blue		
yellow		

Draw a graph.

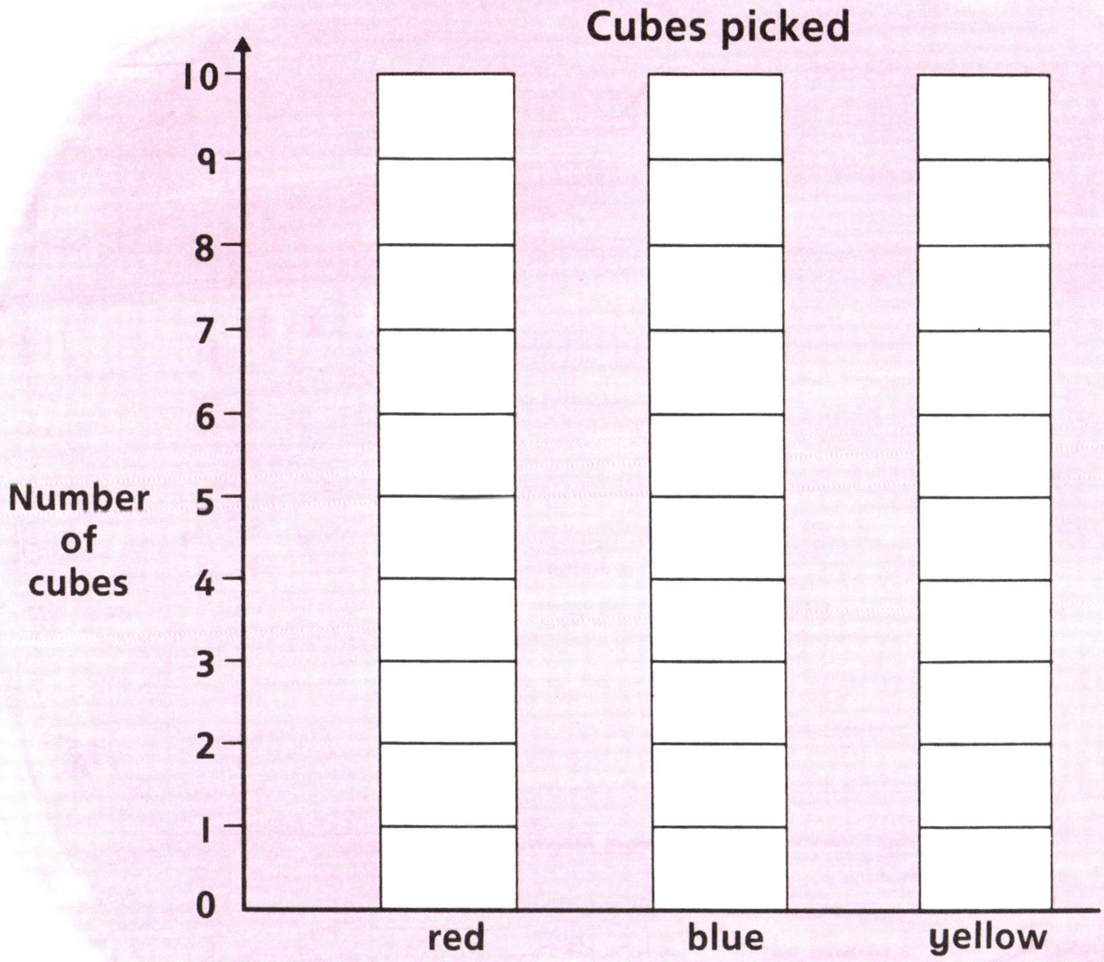

Cubes picked

Number of cubes

red   blue   yellow

Constructing a frequency table

Shapes

You need the bag of shapes.

Pick a shape. Tick its name.

Do this until the bag is empty.

Shape	Ticks (✓)	Number of shapes
 cubes		
 cones		
 spheres		
 pyramids		

Draw a graph.

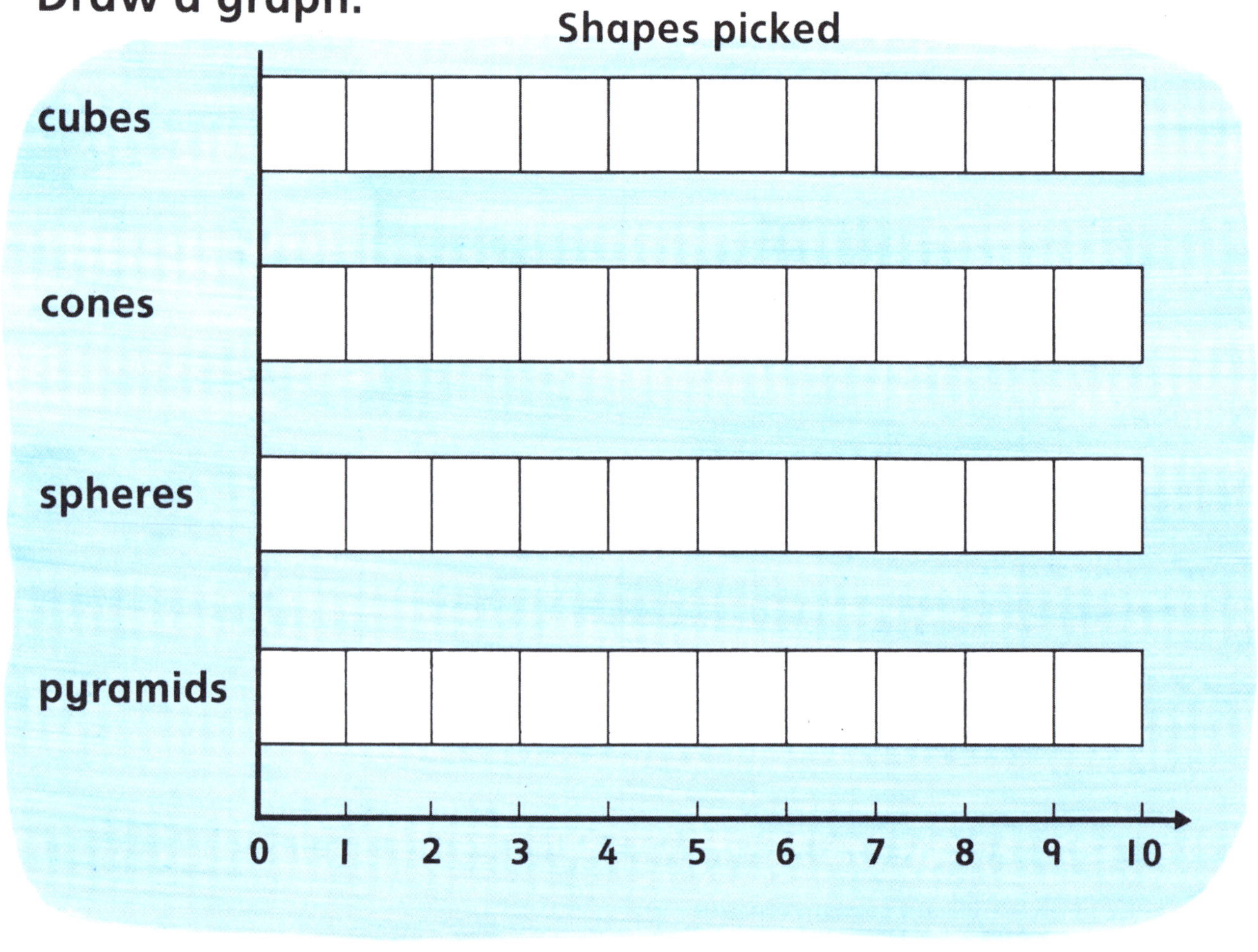

Shapes picked

cubes

cones

spheres

pyramids

0 1 2 3 4 5 6 7 8 9 10

Pirates

Write the names of the pirates.

	beard	no beard
parrot	Jake	
no parrot		

Dolls

Draw on each doll what she is wearing.

	hat	no hat
necklace	Patti Kate	Sally Jill
no necklace	Lyn	May

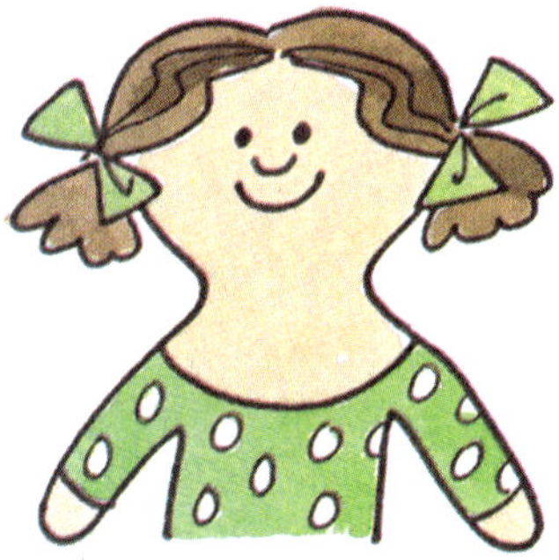

Sally

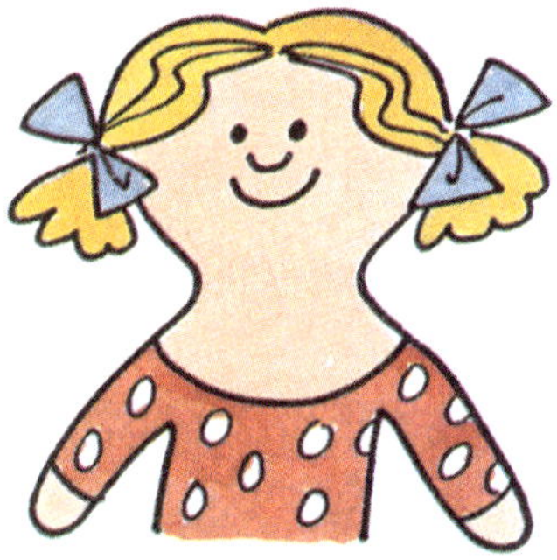

Patti

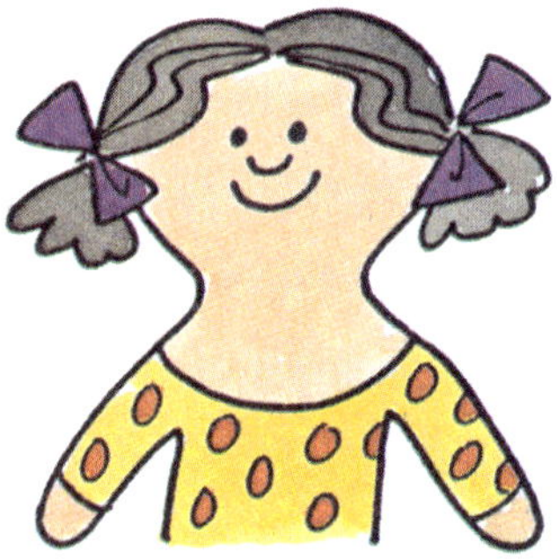

May

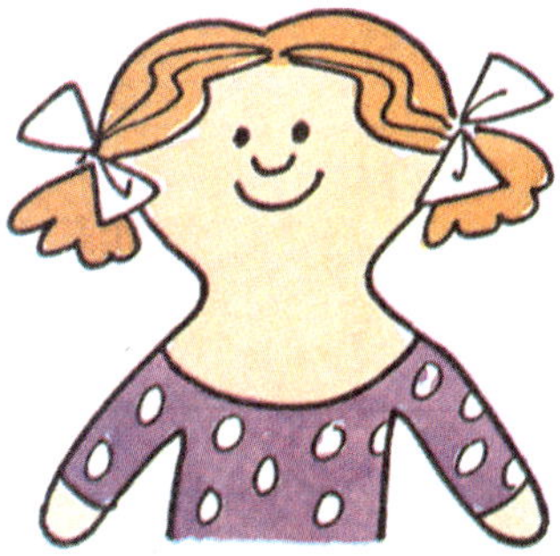

Jill

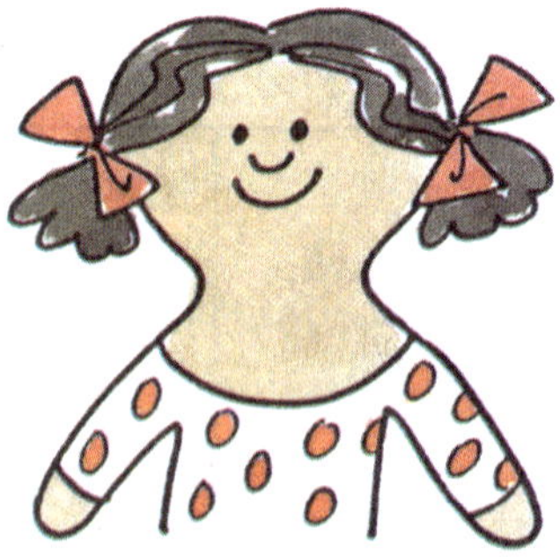

Lyn

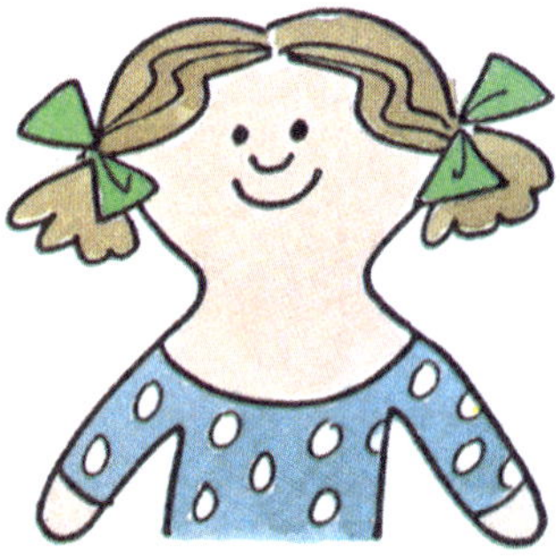

Kate

1	2	3	4	5	6	7	8	9	10	11	12	13	14	15

Heinemann is an imprint of Pearson Education Limited, a company incorporated in England and Wales, having its registered office at Edinburgh Gate, Harlow, Essex, CM20 2JE. Registered company number: 872828
ISBN 978 0 435 03097 1
First published 1991. Revised edition 1995. 25 34
Typeset and Illustrated by Oxprint Design. Printed and bound in Great Britain by Bell & Bain Ltd, Glasgow

ISBN 978-0-435030-97-1